THE NERVOUS PERSON'S C

DR KENNETH HAMBLY grew up and trained as a doctor in Northern Ireland. He has since worked as a gynaecologist and a general practitioner in Canada, England and Scotland, and he currently practises in Ayrshire. He has studied the relationship between physical symptoms and emotional problems in detail, and he is the author of *Overcoming Tension* and *How to Improve Your Confidence*, both also published by Sheldon Press.

Overcoming Common Problems Series

The ABC of Eating
Coping with anorexia, bulimia and compulsive eating
JOY MELVILLE

An A–Z of Alternative Medicine
BRENT Q. HAFEN AND KATHRYN J. FRANDSEN

Arthritis
Is your suffering really necessary?
DR WILLIAM FOX

Being the Boss
STEPHEN FITZ-SIMON

Birth Over Thirty
SHEILA KITZINGER

Body Language
How to read others' thoughts by their gestures
ALLAN PEASE

Calm Down
How to cope with frustration and anger
DR PAUL HAUCK

Comfort for Depression
JANET HORWOOD

Common Childhood Illnesses
DR PATRICIA GILBERT

Complete Public Speaker
GILES BRANDRETH

Coping with Depression and Elation
DR PATRICK McKEON

Coping Successfully with Your Child's Asthma
DR PAUL CARSON

Coping Successfully with Your Child's Skin Problems
DR PAUL CARSON

Coping Successfully with Your Hyperactive Child
DR PAUL CARSON

Curing Arthritis Cookbook
MARGARET HILLS

Curing Arthritis – The Drug-free Way
MARGARET HILLS

Curing Illness – The Drug-free Way
MARGARET HILLS

Depression
DR PAUL HAUCK

Divorce and Separation
ANGELA WILLANS

The Epilepsy Handbook
SHELAGH McGOVERN

Everything You Need to Know about Adoption
MAGGIE JONES

Everything You Need to Know about Contact Lenses
DR ROBERT YOUNGSON

Everything You Need to Know about Your Eyes
DR ROBERT YOUNGSON

Everything You Need to Know about the Pill
WENDY COOPER AND TOM SMITH

Everything You Need to Know about Shingles
DR ROBERT YOUNGSON

Family First Aid and Emergency Handbook
DR ANDREW STANWAY

Fears and Phobias
What they are and how to overcome them
DR TONY WHITEHEAD

Feverfew
A traditional herbal remedy for migraine and arthritis
DR STEWART JOHNSON

Fight Your Phobia and Win
DAVID LEWIS

Flying Without Fear
TESSA DUCKWORTH AND DAVID MILLER

Goodbye Backache
DR DAVID IMRIE WITH COLLEEN DIMSON

Good Publicity Guide
REGINALD PEPLOW

Helping Children Cope with Grief
ROSEMARY WELLS

Overcoming Common Problems Series

How to Be Your Own Best Friend
DR PAUL HAUCK

How to Bring up your Child Successfully
DR PAUL HAUCK

How to Control your Drinking
DRS W. MILLER AND R. MUNOZ

How to Cope with Stress
DR PETER TYRER

How to Cope with your Child's Allergies
DR PAUL CARSON

How to Cope with your Nerves
DR TONY LAKE

How to Cope with Tinnitus and Hearing Loss
DR ROBERT YOUNGSON

How to Do What You Want to Do
DR PAUL HAUCK

How to Enjoy Your Old Age
DR B. F. SKINNER AND M. E. VAUGHAN

How to Improve Your Confidence
DR KENNETH HAMBLY

How to Interview and Be Interviewed
MICHELE BROWN AND GYLES BRANDRETH

How to Love a Difficult Man
NANCY GOOD

How to Love and be Loved
DR PAUL HAUCK

How to Say No to Alcohol
KEITH McNEILL

How to Sleep Better
DR PETER TYRER

How to Stand up for Yourself
DR PAUL HAUCK

How to Start a Conversation and Make Friends
DON GABOR

How to Stop Feeling Guilty
DR VERNON COLEMAN

How to Stop Smoking
GEORGE TARGET

How to Stop Taking Tranquillisers
DR PETER TYRER

If Your Child is Diabetic
JOANNE ELLIOTT

Jealousy
DR PAUL HAUCK

Learning to Live with Multiple Sclerosis
DR ROBERT POVEY, ROBIN DOWIE AND GILLIAN PRETT

Living with Grief
DR TONY LAKE

Living Through Personal Crisis
ANN KAISER STEARNS

Living with High Blood Pressure
DR TOM SMITH

Loneliness
DR TONY LAKE

Making Marriage Work
DR PAUL HAUCK

Making the Most of Loving
GILL COX AND SHEILA DAINOW

Making the Most of Middle Age
DR BRICE PITT

Making the Most of Yourself
GILL COX AND SHEILA DAINOW

Making Relationships Work
CHRISTINE SANDFORD AND WYN BEARDSLEY

Meeting People is Fun
How to overcome shyness
DR PHYLLIS SHAW

One Parent Families
DIANA DAVENPORT

Overcoming Stress
DR VERNON COLEMAN

Overcoming Tension
DR KENNETH HAMBLY

The Parkinson's Disease Handbook
DR RICHARD GODWIN-AUSTEN

Second Wife, Second Best?
Managing your marriage as a second wife
GLYNNIS WALKER

Overcoming Common Problems Series

Self-Help for your Arthritis
EDNA PEMBLE

Six Weeks to a Healthy Back
ALEXANDER MELLEBY

Sleep Like a Dream – The Drug-Free Way
ROSEMARY NICOL

Solving your Personal Problems
PETER HONEY

A Step-Parent's Handbook
KATE RAPHAEL

Stress and your Stomach
DR VERNON COLEMAN

Trying to Have a Baby?
Overcoming infertility and child loss
MAGGIE JONES

What Everyone Should Know about Drugs
KENNETH LEECH

Why Be Afraid?
How to overcome your fears
DR PAUL HAUCK

You and Your Varicose Veins
DR PATRICIA GILBERT

Your Arthritic Hip and You
GEORGE TARGET

Overcoming Common Problems

THE NERVOUS PERSON'S COMPANION

Dr Kenneth Hambly

M.B., B.Ch., M.R.C.O.G.

SHELDON PRESS
LONDON

First published in Great Britain in 1988 by
Sheldon Press, SPCK, Marylebone Road, London NW1 4DU

British Library Cataloguing in Publication Data

Hambly, Kenneth
The nervous person's companion.
1. Man. Phobias. Self-treatment
I. Title II. Series
616.85'225068

ISBN 0-85969-581-6

Photoset by Deltatype Ltd, Ellesmere Port, Cheshire
Printed in Great Britain by Richard Clay Ltd, Bungay, Suffolk

for my daughters
Caroline, Catherine and Corinne

Contents

Introduction
How This Book Can Help

If you have always been a nervous person, or if for various reasons you have become nervous recently, you may have all sorts of problems. You aren't the only nervous person in the world, and you certainly aren't the only person with problems, but it can feel like that. It can be very difficult to explain to other people just what you feel like, and how severe your problems can be. It is difficult for others to really understand what is happening to you unless they have experienced something similar themselves. So you feel very alone.

It is bad enough to be tense and nervous without having to deal with a feeling of isolation as well. But why should *you* feel isolated and alone when so many other people have the same problems? Why is it so difficult for people to understand that a nervous person can have real and often severe symptoms which are caused by an overactive nervous system?

If you are leading a life which is limited by your nervous problems, or even if you are leading a normal life despite episodes of severe discomfort, it is time you did something about your problems. Of course that isn't easy, and you might even have tried and failed in the past, possibly because you have gone about things the wrong way. But if you take a different line, you can solve your problems. You can get back to living a normal life without the discomfort and the fear which is making your life a misery now.

There is no reason why you should feel isolated and alone. Your problems are common to all those who sometimes feel tense and anxious, and they are many. They experience the same symptoms in public places as you do. They may have found that talking to people about their problems is useless because others just don't want to know. That is because everyone feels tense, or nervous, or frightened at some time in his or her life, and don't want to be reminded of that. When approached, such people simply 'back off'.

But you *aren't* alone. There *are* people who understand your problems, or who have similar problems of their own. Often they have learned not to talk about them because of the way other people have reacted. Such people may get together in 'self-help' groups, and these can be very useful. But such a group can only meet occasionally, and it can only provide limited support because the members of that group can't be with you when your problems are at their worst.

It would be good to have a companion who could be with you at times when things are bad, to give you advice on the spot. Hopefully, that is just what this little book will provide. Sometimes a book can be the best companion. It doesn't demand anything. It is simply there to offer advice and perhaps comfort. It is there if you need it. You can refer to it when you want to, at any time and in any place. It will offer the advice that an understanding friend might offer. It will tell you what you want to know when you really want to know it.

How have you got into this situation, where you feel anxious and tense, when going on a bus or a train can be difficult, or where going to a meeting, a cinema, a supermarket, bank or post office, can cause uncomfortable symptoms? Why is so much of your life a misery? Is there something seriously wrong with you? How can you get your life back on the right track?

If you have an overactive nervous system, you will eventually experience unpleasant symptoms in certain stressful situations. That doesn't mean that there is anything *seriously* wrong with you, even though your symptoms may be very severe. We could discuss for hours the reasons why these happen, but it is probably enough for you to understand that you *have* an overactive nervous system. In these difficult situations your body produces a potent substance called adrenaline which can raise your blood pressure, make you sweat, make your stomach churn ('butterflies'), give you a tremor and produce muscle tension. No wonder there are times when the tense person doesn't feel too well.

The main problem is that a nervous or tense person still has to live his or her life, despite the difficulties. He or she still has to go out, go to meetings and social gatherings. It takes a lot of courage to do that. It is hard to keep going, and yet the alternative is to sit at home and do nothing. Most tense people do the best they can, and they get very little encouragement or help. They may live restricted lives because there are some activities, like perhaps going abroad on holiday, which they feel they just can't do.

No one should have to live a life restricted by their nerves. Everyone has the right to a full and happy life, and there is no reason why he or she should not have one. Problems are there to be solved. All that is needed is the determination to set about solving them, the right way. That is what this book is all about.

This book will give you advice, help and encouragement when you need it. It will help you to solve your problems the right way, so that you can overcome your difficulties and get back to a normal way of life. The first chapter tells you how you can cope at home, but after that it deals with going out into the world and living a normal life.

It is only by going out into the world and facing situations that you may find difficult that you can defeat your symptoms, regain confidence, and return to a normal life. It isn't easy, but it *is* possible with help. And this book will give you that help.

It is my hope that you will soon be able to throw this book away. When you have done that it will have served its purpose. You will be comfortable in the situations that you previously found difficult. You will be able to lead a full life. You will have got rid of that awful fear of what 'might happen'. If this is what *you* want to achieve, then the sooner you start the better.

1
Making a Start

There is always a 'first of all', always something we have to do before we get on to the more exciting bits. Tackling your problem is just like everything else. First of all you have to practise. After that you can get on with what you really find difficult. So let's make a start.

There are three things you can do at home. When you *have* done them everything else is easier:

- Understand your problem
- Learn relaxation exercises
- Learn breathing exercises

When you have spent just a little time practising these things you can start to use them in real-world situations. They will be of immense help to you and give you greatly improved confidence. It is well worth the time and effort spent on them. Of course you may have heard it all before. After all, there's nothing new under the sun. But this time the exercises are going to be used for a purpose. It is just a step for us into the world outside. We shall start with a brief description of the problem, and make sure that we agree on exactly what we are dealing with.

Understanding your problem

You are an anxious, nervous person. That means that you have an overactive nervous system, and get unpleasant symptoms much of the time. These symptoms are worse in certain situations such as supermarket queues or perhaps in the bank. Or you may not particularly like crowds.

Why do you get these symptoms? They happen because most of your nervous system works automatically so you aren't aware of it at all. At least that's the way it *should* be. For some people their nervous system isn't quite so automatic and they are more aware of it than others. You may be one of these people.

For example, we all need a certain amount of tension or 'tone' in our muscles. If that tension wasn't there we would fold up and fall over. As we walk that tension is released in some muscles and tightened up in others, automatically. But for some of us our nervous system, which controls the tone in our muscles, overreacts and we become overtense. This tension lasts for a long time and we may remain tense even in our sleep. All anxious people experience this and it is a major cause of problems. That is why we have to learn to relax actively.

Our nervous system can also cause other symptoms such as diarrhoea, a tremor, sweating and, worst of all, panic attacks. In these attacks we feel a wave of panic, dizziness and shakiness. It can be very disturbing. So we have to regain control of our nervous system and use that control in public. We do that by learning to relax and to breathe.

Learning relaxation exercises

Here we shall describe one method of relaxing. Of course, there are others. If you have been pregnant you will have learned antenatal exercises, or maybe you have taken yoga classes; these techniques will do just as well, as long as you have something you can do at times of stress. Learn and practise these exercises at home. Do them by yourself in a quiet warm room and initially allow about twenty minutes for them.

Sit in a good chair with your head supported, or else lie down on a bed. Make sure that you are comfortable. Try to relax for a moment or two. Then begin the exercises.

Begin by squeezing your right fist. Tighten it up. Hold it tight for a few seconds. Now relax it suddenly. Feel the relaxation come into your arm right up to your shoulder. Enjoy that feeling of relaxation. Now go to your left hand. Make a fist and tighten it up. Hold that for a few seconds and then relax it suddenly. Feel and enjoy the feeling of relaxation in your arm and shoulder. Slow your breathing.

Now pull your shoulders up and hold them. Relax them. Feel the relaxation coming into your shoulders and neck. Enjoy that feeling and slow your breathing. Breathe slowly and deeply.

Now to your neck. It is often your neck which is most stiff and tense. Push your neck back and hold it there. Tighten your neck muscles and hold them tight for a moment. Now relax them suddenly and enjoy that feeling. Breathe slowly. You have to practise and keep practising.

Next tighten up your facial muscles. Make a frown. Clench your teeth and wrinkle your forehead. Hold that, then quickly relax the muscles and slow your breathing. Enjoy the relaxation.

Move on to your stomach. Pull it in, making yourself as slim as possible. Hold that position, and then relax. Slow your breathing.

Lastly it is the turn of your legs. Push your toes into the floor, or push them away from you if you are lying down. This will tighten up all the muscles in your legs. Don't hold it too long or you might get cramp in your legs and that would spoil everything. Relax your legs and enjoy the feeling of relaxation.

You have now finished the exercises, except for breathing. You have been slowing your breathing down during the exercises. Continue to do this. You should be able to reduce your breathing to about eight breaths a minute. This will increase your feeling of relaxation. Don't expect to be able to achieve total relaxation straight away. It takes time and daily practice, but when you have achieved it you will feel warm and comfortable, almost floating. It is a very pleasant sensation for an habitually tense person.

Continue your relaxation session by thinking warm relaxing thoughts. Think about a warm beach or a luxurious bed. Think relaxation. Think 'slow down'. Take it easy. Now it is time to stop. Count down, 'three, two, one, wake-up'—you are back in the real world. You may feel relaxed and refreshed, but that is not really the point. You are learning a technique that you will be able to use anywhere, a technique that you can take with you whenever you have to face a difficult situation, just as you might take this book. You have to be able to relax on a bus or in a meeting. Eventually you have to be able to relax automatically, so that relaxation becomes the norm instead of the tension you usually feel. All it needs is daily practice. You must do that and *you must stick to it*. No excuses. It is an important first step.

Learning breathing exercises

These exercises are briefer and can be done while watching television, for example. Some people habitually overbreathe. This causes changes in the blood which lead to muscle tension. Such people have to re-educate their breathing, and it is worth while learning the technique, because the more control you have over your body the more confident you will feel.

Sit quietly, preferably in front of the television set. Most people don't use their chest muscles for breathing when they are at rest. That seems odd but it is true. They breathe by using their stomach muscles, and their chest stays still and relaxed.

To see *how* you breathe, place one hand on your chest and one on your stomach. At rest your stomach hand should be seen moving, and your chest hand should stay still. You should be breathing quietly, not sighing, yawning or taking frequent deep breaths. Stay in this position for several minutes.

Try to concentrate on the hand on your stomach. Try to relax and breathe evenly and slowly, and with your stomach muscles. Try to relax away any yawns or sighs. Just let that abdominal hand go up and down. Try to cultivate normal breathing at rest, and breathe in and out slowly and evenly. If it helps, sit in a 'slouched' position, half reclining. Keep up that normal, quiet even breathing for as long as you can, so that it becomes a habit. This book is all about learning good habits and forgetting about the old bad habits.

What next?

Now it's time to get out into the world and start living a normal life. That is what you want to do and what you *should* be doing. There is a limit to what you can achieve in the privacy of your own home. You really do have to tackle things you find difficult. You *can* practise them in your imagination at home. You can use that time after you have done your relaxation exercises, when you are deeply relaxed, to think about the difficult problems you might have to face the next day. You can go over them in your mind, keeping yourself relaxed, and work out your approach. You can imagine yourself in a difficult situation and go through everything in your mind.

If you are imaginative, you can recreate that situation in your imagination and experience every sensation that you might experience in the real situation. You can then practise controlling your sensations and this may help you later. But you still have to go out and face the world. A few tricks of the trade may be of help. You have your new skills of relaxation. You have your own courage and determination. All these things will get you through the day.

Remember: none of the unpleasant sensations or symptoms you may experience can do you any harm. You just have to learn to live with them and deal with them. That's easy to say and difficult to do. That's why this book has been written to help you. And you need a little help at the moment. Soon you will be able to manage on your own.

Don't try to read the rest of the book right through. Refer to it as you need to. Dip into it when the situation requires it. Use it in any way you want. But first you must stop avoiding difficult situations. You may not even be aware that you are doing this, but in many small ways you almost certainly are. Start now to live a strictly normal life without restriction. Entertain visitors at home. Book that holiday. Accept that invitation. Go out to the cinema or theatre. Now is the time. Don't put it off.

2
Being at Home

Some people have problems just being at home. Particular problems might be entertaining, or wind noise in a storm, or even the telephone ringing. Nervous problems can be difficult to understand or explain. Your own home should feel safe. Most of the time it is. But there may be some times, perhaps weekends, when it is less than comfortable for you.

Your home should be a comfortable pleasant place. It is important for it to be so because you spend so much of your time there. If you have problems at home this chapter will help you.

Let us look at the following areas:

- Being alone
- An unexpected caller
- Entertaining
- Noise
- Weekends
- Children
- The telephone

Being alone

Women spend more time by themselves in the house than men. Often they may spend the greater part of the day alone. If you are in this situation, you may find being alone rather difficult. It is that moment when your husband and perhaps your children have left the house in the morning. They are off to school and to work and here you are by yourself. The house can feel very empty and you can feel very alone.

In all the situations we will discuss, it's the physical discomfort that is the most difficult thing to deal with, the muscle tightness and the churning stomach. If you are alone in the house there is no one to watch you so you don't have the problem of putting on a brave face, but that can cause problems in itself. There just isn't anyone to talk to and the feeling of isolation can be just as bad as it might be if you were outside and feeling alone and vulnerable.

This discomfort builds up. You decide that you won't let it bother you, but you can't control what you think about, can you? You may experience increasing agitation with unpleasant symptoms. The usual response to this situation is to start to work harder and faster, perhaps hoovering and cleaning the entire house. That is the worst possible thing you could do, and simply makes you tighter and more and more uncomfortable.

What you *must* do in this situation is sit down quietly and relax. You should have been practising relaxation exercises at a time when you are at your most comfortable so you will have experience of doing them. Now is the time to use them. Play some relaxing music and slow your breathing. Regain control of your body.

When you feel comfortable, start to do the housework in a slow relaxed way.

Entertaining

We all entertain people at home sometimes. It might just be giving a neighbour a cup of coffee, or it might be entertaining the boss and his wife when a promotion is in the offing. Some of us are natural entertainers on or off the stage, and some of us are not. Whatever the situation, we want to entertain well and to give the best impression we can, even if we are literally terrified at the prospect of what we have to do and feel that we really can't go through with it.

How *can* we get through the evening? Surely the whole thing will be a disaster? Certainly not. At worst, you will probably manage very well, and at best you will have an excellent evening which you will genuinely enjoy and remember. The secret is in careful planning. You have to plan the evening in detail and be prepared to deal calmly with anything that goes wrong.

Decide when you are going to entertain, and whom you are going to invite. Decide what you are going to eat and how you are going to prepare it. What about drink? Are you going to have wine? Think of all the details and do as much of the preparation in advance as you can. Make sure you have made definite, easily understood arrangements, so that your guests know what time to come (and on what day), who will be there, and what sort of a meal they can expect.

Now the arrival of your guests is getting near and you are becoming uncomfortable. Everybody tends to do this. You have an advantage over most because you have learned relaxation exercises. Sit quietly waiting for your probably delayed guests. You might have one sherry, but stay sober. Stay in command. Have the music on and the meal cooking.

Your guests arrive. They are a little flustered, just like you. They give you their coats and sit down. Offer them a drink, alcoholic or non-alcoholic, and stay relaxed. Resist the tendency to talk too much. Allow silences to happen in the conversation. If *you* can relax, your guests will relax. You can introduce topics of conversation, perhaps about the music or about artefacts in the room, or something that happened today. But don't overdo it.

If you have to leave the room for any reason, just say 'Excuse me', and walk out. Don't explain or make complicated excuses. If you just leave quietly no one will notice that you've gone, or if they do they will assume that there is a simple reason for your departure. Come back when you want to and carry on as before. If you don't draw attention to yourself, people don't notice what you are doing. They are much too interested in what they are doing themselves, or in what they are saying or intending to say.

And will you panic and make a fool of yourself? What do

you think? You may feel bad, but you will look perfectly well. Practise talking slowly and staying calm. Ride out those panic attacks. As the evening goes on you will relax more and more and everything will become easier.

Noise

Noise can be oppressive (as indeed can silence). Some people find it physically distressing. They just can't stand the television blasting or the record player blaring away, and in this day and age that is what happens a lot of the time, particularly if there are teenagers or young adults around. They are becoming a generation with impaired hearing because of their constant exposure to pop music. Still, there's no reason why *you* should have to put up with it.

There may be occasions when you can't avoid noise, wind noise or thunder for example, so you should practise managing that situation. Do it when you are feeling good, listen to loud noise and do it often. You will soon get used to noise and be comfortable with it, for a short time at least.

Weekends

What about weekends? That is the time when you should be relaxed and at ease. Surely everyone knows that? Well not quite. Some people feel at their worst at weekends, and may even have difficulty coping, for many reasons.

The main difficulty at weekends is probably just that everybody is at home, hanging around and getting on each other's nerves. Sometimes it is the husband and father who is out at work all week and just wants a relaxing time at home. He can't get it because the family don't share his idea of a relaxing time. They prefer to play records and make a lot of noise, and to stay out late and bring friends home.

Or it may be the mother who is used to having the house to herself and resents the intrusion into what all week has been her world. Her family render it noisy and untidy. A weekend can seem a very long time.

You don't have to spend all your weekend in the close proximity of your family. If that is difficult for you, arrange to go out for part of the weekend. Arrange to spend some time by yourself. Take a close look at your feelings and your difficulties and arrange your weekend to accommodate them. That doesn't mean avoiding the situation. Practise being relaxed, but if you are having problems, take the dog for that long walk, or perhaps retire to the kitchen shooing the others out.

Children

We all like children, particularly our own. But do we have to like them the same way all the time? Children can be very wearing as any parent can testify. Nervous people are often overconscientious and don't make the allowances that others might make, so they feel guilty when their tempers run short and have feelings about their own children which they don't like to admit they have.

Such feelings are normal. Everyone can feel anger and resentment at people they love and there is no need to feel guilty about it. Acceptance is a fine thing, and so long as your feelings are not too unreasonable, just allow them to happen. If you are still unhappy about the strength of your feelings, make arrangements to be away from your children, or other people's children if that is the problem, for a time.

The telephone

The telephone is there for your convenience. Some nervous people find it difficult to handle. The ring (or bleep) of the telephone makes them jump. They dread the sound. They are nervous answering it, and feel that they are choking.

Making a call is no easier. They have a tremor when they

dial. It is worse if they have to speak to someone important. The telephone has become a problem.

The telephone should be your friend. If it has begun to cause you problems you should start to deal with them. How do you do that? It is just the same as with most of these difficult things: you practise. That isn't difficult with the telephone. You can wait for a quiet time and phone anyone you like. How about the speaking clock, or the cricket score? Then move on to phoning a friend. Practice makes perfect, or at least easier.

* * *

Most people find that they are uneasy if they are left on their own. Many people feel just a little uneasy when they have to phone someone they don't know, or if they have to talk on the telephone when others are listening. A lot of people feel harassed at weekends. The experiences you have and the things you feel aren't that unusual or difficult to understand. It's all a matter of degree. You might feel these things a little more than other people do, or get more severe physical sensations than others, even feel that you aren't in control of your body all of the time the way you would like to be. This isn't the end of the world. If you work at it you can overcome these problems. It isn't easy, but it's worth the effort.

3
Travelling

For a nervous person the most simple things can appear difficult. Even leaving the security of one's own home and going for a walk can cause problems. Going out is the first step in achieving anything and it is a hurdle which has to be overcome. In this life we have to travel and to go places. It is part of the enjoyment of life. The advice given in this chapter may seem straightforward and even obvious to some, but if you are a nervous person you will know how difficult simple things can be, and how important it is to go about things the right way. It should be possible to go out and to travel just like anyone else. It isn't easy if you are habitually tense. The way to overcome that tension is to practise as often as possible, and to follow the advice in this chapter.

Let us look at various areas that involve travelling:

- Going out
- Panic attacks
- Travelling by car
- Travelling by bus
- Going by train

Going out

Anticipation

Before you go anywhere you have to actually leave the house, and for you that may not be easy. Some people are house-bound because they are too nervous to go out. Some people can only go out if accompanied by a friend. Many more people just feel uneasy and uncomfortable about going out. They may have diarrhoea and feel shaky, as if something terrible were going to happen. If you are a nervous person then you will certainly get these feelings from time to time.

Like almost everything else in a nervous person's life, the anticipation is worse than the event. The problem for you is just getting out. Things aren't so bad when you do get out. It's the '*what if?*' phenomenon. What will happen if I faint? What will happen if I meet someone? What will happen if I break down in the shop? You may not actually have these thoughts, but your body does. Even before you have decided to go out, it seems as if your nervous system has gone into top gear and you are off. Sometimes these feelings may actually stop you from going out.

Leaving the house

What do you do about it? You decide that you *are* going to go out. That may be a big decision. Decide where you are going to go. If you aren't used to going out you might just want to go round the corner and back. Chose the easiest route you can think of, even if it's only a few yards. *Don't change your mind*, no matter how bad you may feel.

If you are in the habit of going back into the toilet because that feeling of diarrhoea persists, delay doing it. Your intestine may be overworking but you haven't got real diarrhoea. You can retrain your intestine by waiting to see if you really do need to go, and only going when you have to, probably not very often. After only a few days you can prolong the time between visits to the toilet until the problem has virtually gone away.

Before you go out, sit down. Relax. What is your body doing? It may be overworking but so what? Slow everything down. Don't pace up and down. Don't talk too much. Don't look for things you know you have. Walk slowly, talk slowly, open the door slowly and out you go. What was all the fuss about?

Going out will be easier the next time. Develop a routine and stick to it. Go a little further each day and watch your confidence build. Now you are out there, there is nothing you cannot achieve.

Going somewhere special

Going out isn't an end in itself, of course. Most of the time we go out in order to do something or to go somewhere special. It may be to visit friends or relatives or to go to a concert or to the cinema. Sometimes these events are stressful in themselves and so going to them can be unpleasant. You might have symptoms such as an upset stomach for many hours before going out. As the time to leave the house approaches you might feel that you won't be able to go after all. You might be thinking of excuses which would allow you to stay in the safety of your home.

Accept that going out will be difficult, and that the most difficult bit may be leaving the house. Get ready early and allow plenty of time. Decide at what time you are going to leave the house and go at that time. Take things easy. Sit quietly and relax for a few minutes before you go out. Don't keep going to the toilet or checking your tickets. Do things deliberately once only.

Now the time has come to go. Simply stand up, open the front door, and out you go. As soon as you are under way you will feel better. We will talk about any problems you might have at your destination later.

Panic attacks

If you have a tendency to get panic attacks, when your heart speeds up and you sweat and tremble, then you might have one while you are out. Always remember that a panic attack can do you *no harm*, even though it is unpleasant. If you have a panic attack stand still for a moment or two. If you feel you need to, lean against the wall. A panic attack will not last for more than a few seconds and then it will pass, leaving you feeling a little weak and unsteady. When it has passed, pick yourself up and carry on. You will be none the worse for wear.

Panic attacks are frightening, but no one will know that you are having one if you don't want them to. Just act normally and people will think that nothing is the matter. It is quite possible to have a panic attack while talking to someone without them being aware that anything is wrong. You may have that constant feeling of barely suppressed panic all the time, which can be very unpleasant, or even frightening. You have to get used to that feeling if you are a nervous person. Accept it, get used to it, carry on as if it doesn't exist.

The worst thing about being out in public is that feeling of exposure, the feeling that there is 'nowhere to hide'. You just feel downright uncomfortable and uneasy, feel that something is going to happen, that you are going to be ill or that you might make a fool of yourself. You just have to get used to this feeling of discomfort. Sometimes it will be worse than others. Treat it like a grumpy friend. It is always there so you have to learn to live with it. Disregard it and go on walking further and doing more. You have nothing to lose.

Travelling by car

Travelling by car either as a driver or as a passenger can be equally bad if you are a nervous person. Some people find it easier to be the driver, some the passenger. Some find it easier to sit in the front seat, while others prefer sitting in the back.

As a driver

If you are a nervous driver you will probably have no difficulty with everyday driving, but some aspects will make your heart speed up and make you feel nervous. Speed is one thing. Overtaking or being caught in the fast lane on a dual carriageway is another. Some people get nervous going over bridges, or under bridges, or going under high tension electric power lines. Some drivers may feel nervous approaching a roundabout. As with all of these nervous phenomena, there is no logic at all.

What do you do about your problems if you are a driver? That can be tricky. You can't avoid the situations that might cause you difficulty. But you can drive in a way that will make them less likely to happen provided that isn't dangerous in itself. Avoiding difficult situations is never the answer. The answer is to practise what you find difficult. Do it as often as you can, using all the relaxation techniques you have learned. Drive for short distances on the motorway or bypass if you can. Drive fast for short distances if the road is clear. Go into the outside lane if the traffic is slow. Relax and take your own time. Get used to the sensations you may have. Learn to live with them and to drive safely with them.

Learn to relax in the car, using the relaxation exercises you have practised at home. Let your shoulders go loose. Move your head around and loosen up your neck. Breathe slowly and enjoy the sensation of relaxation.

If you do get caught in a situation that makes you feel panicky, *don't* panic, not if you're driving. You won't, in fact, because your instinct is not to do so. You won't do anything sudden. You will wait for your opportunity and you will do the correct thing according to the traffic conditions at the time. That's what other people do.

As a passenger

If your problems are as a passenger then the situation isn't so difficult. You may be uncomfortable but you don't have to *do* anything. You aren't responsible for the safety of others. All you have to do is to sit there, breathe slowly and relax. Allow time for things to settle down. Remember that nothing can happen to you. You will just be miserable, but you will survive.

Travelling by bus

Travelling on a bus can be *nervewracking*. It happens in public and it involves movement. You have to deal with paying the driver and you have to be sure to get on the right bus and to get off at the right stop. You are carried further from home and you are trapped on the bus. At least it feels like that. Of course you *aren't* trapped. You can get off at any stop and you can even get off between stops if you tell the driver that you are going to be sick. You may feel conspicuous but you aren't. People avoid looking at each other on public transport.

Waiting for the bus may be the worst part. When will it come? Will it come? Can I be sure it's the right bus? Will I be able to get on? Will I have the right money? Will I be able to stay on? Will I faint? Will I make a fool of myself? The waiting is terrible. Ask yourself all the questions I have asked and answer them honestly. Yes you will get on, and no you won't make an exhibition of yourself. When did you last see someone do that on a bus?

The bus arrives. Practise your speech to the driver. Get on, ignoring your rapid pulse. Pay your money and sit down, perhaps near to the door. To stay on the bus just sit there and practise slowing your breathing and relaxing. Nothing can happen to you. You may panic but so what? You may feel terrible but you will look all right.

If you know the route or if you have done your homework you will know when your stop is due. Keep an eye out for landmarks, and when your stop comes signal to the driver and stand up. When the bus stops, get off, and congratulate yourself on what you have achieved. The next time will be easier.

Travelling by train

Travelling by train is much like travelling by bus, but for some people it is more difficult. You can't go to the driver of an express train and tell him you want to get off because you feel sick, can you?

The problems can start at the ticket office. You may have to queue and queueing can be a problem for many people. If you are travelling with someone else he or she could buy your ticket for you. You have to deal with other people like the ticket office clerk. You have to pay and exchange money. Then you have to wait in a crowd on the platform for the train, and the arrival of the train is a dramatic event.

Modern trains are not designed for nervous people. The old trains were better, with their compartments and corridors where you could find privacy. Nowadays trains tend to be packed. Seats can be hard to find, and if you have to go anywhere on the train you have to walk up a central aisle in full view of everyone. There is virtually no privacy. And if you want something to eat you may have to walk through seven or eight carriages.

What do you do if someone sits down beside you? Don't make converstion unless it is appropriate. It might be sensible to wait for the other person to speak first. Then just say as much or as little as you want to. If someone else is forcing his/her attention on you, you can discreetly change your seat, or if that is difficult, just register your disapproval with a look. Always have a magazine or a newspaper with you behind which you can hide if necessary.

So you should travel by train because it is quick and fun despite the disadvantages, and because you want to go somewhere. And because you *can* do it.

* * *

if travelling is a problem, start to deal with it. A problem is there to be solved. It isn't easy but it is essential if you are to lead a normal life. If you want to do anything, from attending a concert to visiting your mother, you have to go out and you have to travel. Practise travelling. Work at it. Expect to be uncomfortable but don't expect anything disastrous to happen. Remember that if you have the courage to start a journey, you will surely arrive.

4
Social Events

Life isn't only about everyday events. It is also about enjoyment and pleasure. People who are nervous can lead difficult lives and they sometimes feel that the 'pleasure factor' has been removed. There just isn't any enjoyment any more. Social events are meant to be enjoyed, and if you aren't enjoying them now it's time you did something about it. And social events aren't *just* for fun. They can be important. You might have to go to a social event related to your employment, and which might be important for either your job or your husband's. Maybe you should get to grips with your problems if they relate to social events.

Going out to a social event can be traumatic. Often you are on show and you are there to be seen and judged. That isn't as difficult or as daunting as it seems. If you are avoiding social events, it's time you started going out . . . *and enjoying yourself*.

Let's look at some aspects of this problem:

- Going out
- Small gatherings in people's houses
- Social events in hotels and public places
- Dining out
- Alcohol
- Meeting people
- Conversation

Going out

Preparation

There is no substitute for preparation. A nervous person has to be better prepared than anyone else, as social events are more traumatic for him or her. Where is the event to be held? Who will be there? What kind of clothes would be appropriate? How long is it likely to last?

Get all these things sorted out in your mind so that there are as few uncertainties as possible. Uncertainties are difficult and unsettling. Get ready in good time. Know that you are prepared and that you look your best. Allow time for a little relaxation. Sit quietly for ten minutes before you are due to leave, and try to judge travelling time accurately so that you can leave home and arrive at your destination both at the right time.

Tell yourself: 'Slow down. Relax your muscles. Breathe slowly and *don't* let yourself get flustered. You will be all right.' And you *will* be all right.

Appearance

For a man appearance isn't too difficult. He really only has to decide if the social event is going to be formal or informal. He usually only has a few choices of clothes. But it is different for a woman. She has to decide what image she wishes to produce. She is judged slightly differently from a man, so there is more opportunity for mistakes and uncertainty.

I think it is better to err on the side of safety, particularly if you aren't too confident. There are people who can go to an Oxfam shop, buy something in which they will look great anywhere. You might well do that, but to carry that sort of thing off you need confidence which you may not have too much of at the moment. It will come.

Dress safely and dress well. That might mean expensively, but you don't go out all that often so it won't be an expense that recurs too frequently—yet. Know that you look well and you will feel well—very important for your confidence.

Small gatherings in other peoples' houses

Small social gatherings can be difficult. In a way you are trapped in the situation. You can't wander out to the bar or take a tour round the grounds. You might feel trapped in a small room. There might be people there you don't particularly like, or it might be hot and uncomfortable.

But at a small party the chances are that you will know everyone, so that difficult introductory period where everyone gets to know everyone else won't be necessary. But watch what happens. Human behaviour is very interesting.

You think that you are the only one who feels uncomfortable at a small party. Watch just how uncomfortable other seemingly confident people seem to be when they arrive. See how they bluster and make aimless conversation.

Every group has an identity, a pecking order with some people leading the conversation and others saying little. That doesn't mean that one person is better than another, because that pecking order changes as time goes on. The group decides to whom it wants to listen, and if someone hogs the conversation he or she will eventually be ignored. It is the person who only speaks where there is something to say whose opinion will be sought. The blusterer has a contribution to make, otherwise the party would be very flat, but so has the quiet person.

Just be yourself. Consciously relax. The worst bit is going up to the front door. Once you are in, a procedure has to be followed which is always the same. You have to be introduced to everyone, you have to find a seat, and you may have to choose a drink. Rehearse it over in your mind in advance and just go through the motions when you arrive.

What about those feelings of panic? You may get them. Nervous people often do. If you feel panicky stop to wonder why. Is it too hot and am I sweating? Do I have feelings of indigestion? Is it too cold? Am I tired? There may be a very good reason why you have unpleasant physical sensations and you shouldn't always interpret them as being the start of a panic attack. But if you do panic, what should you do? Will it ruin the party? Will everyone know and will you be disgraced? Not at all. How do you know how other people are feeling?

Perhaps their piles are bothering them. Perhaps they have 'wind'. Anyway they are far too involved in their own conversation to be watching *you*.

Try to stay in the room if you panic. Breathe slowly and evenly and keep smiling. Panic attacks only last a few seconds and you can survive that length of time. Think of the relief when it's over. A panic attack can do you no harm. You can even carry on a conversation while you are having it. So don't worry. It's your attitude to your problems that is important. Be determined to enjoy yourself and you will. The anticipation is the worst. When you get there it will be fine and you will enjoy it no matter how unlikely that may seem in advance.

Social events in hotels and public places

These can be very different. Wedding receptions and celebration dinners and all sorts of things happen in hotels, clubs or halls, and there are many different places from the really grand to the very ordinary. Each event is different. Such events often involve a formal meal, and that can be a difficulty. Eating in public is dealt with later, as is the management of ceremonies or functions.

If you have to go to an event in such a place, do your homework. What sort of event is it? What will people be wearing? Will there be a meal? Get it right so that there are as few uncertainties as possible. Rehearse the event over in your mind so that nothing comes as a surprise. Remember that you can escape to the lavatory if necessary, or even just take a little walk around the area.

As always, just getting there is the worst bit, particularly if the event is formal. But you *will* get yourself there and as soon as you go through the front door you will start to feel at home. Practise your slow breathing and just relax. All that stomach churning will settle down and, who knows, you might even begin to enjoy yourself.

Dining out

Dining out in hotels or restaurants is a common way of entertaining oneself and others. It may be a big evening occasion or it may be a snack at lunchtime—it doesn't matter, eating in public is a problem for many.

Lunch isn't so bad. It is still eating in public, and there is the possibility of a panic attack or other difficulties, but it is nothing compared to a dinner engagement. Whatever applies to that event also applies in part to that lunch in the snackbar or works cafeteria.

Dining out in the evening starts with the formality of the grand arrival. There is a sense of occasion. Everyone is on show because that is the point of the event. A head waiter or someone in a similar position will conduct your party to your table. Drinks are ordered and produced. By now you maybe feeling as if you are going to die.

You tend to feel panicky because you are hungry. You may feel slightly lightheaded because your blood sugar is a little low. And then your stomach starts to rumble. This is not a minor problem for you the way it might be for someone else, because you are a nervous person. Your stomach rumblings are due to an overactive intestine and that can set off all your feelings of panic.

You will sweat and feel unwell, but stop now and think why? Are you hungry? Is your stomach overworking? Is it hot and are you sweating? All of these things may really be happening and not be caused by your nervousness, but added to this there is your usual problem with conversation and meeting people. No wonder you don't feel so good and why eating out can be difficult. Use all the techniques described previously to help you, and you might well enjoy your meal.

Alcohol

If you don't drink at all you don't need to read this section. If you are a 'social drinker' perhaps you should think about how you use drink for social purposes, as many of us do. Alcohol relaxes people and makes parties go with a swing. It is an established part of our culture.

If you enjoy a drink and are used to drinking and know about your tolerance for alcohol there will be few problems. You just have to be careful to stay within your limits. There is, however, always the temptation to overdo things if you are nervous or anxious. This can produce problems, both long term and short term.

In the long term, if you develop the habit of using drink to relax yourself, you may become an alcoholic. That is not being overdramatic or alarmist. Many alcoholics drink because they cannot manage ordinary social or work problems without drink. If you are beginning to drink too much, stop completely. That is the only answer.

In the short term, if you are tempted to drink too much at a party you will make a fool of yourself. No one really likes a drunk. You want to be in control of yourself, of what you are saying and doing. And you can't drink and drive.

You can have a social drink when you arrive at a social event. You can drink the same as other moderate drinkers and it may help you to relax. There is nothing wrong with that. If you are nervous, you will probably be careful about your drinking, because you will not be happy if things seem to be getting out of control.

Meeting people

Meeting anyone for the first time can be awkward. You are introduced and you immediately forget the person's name because you are nervous. Many people have that problem, but if it is a difficulty for you then you will have to deal with it.

Practise meeting people at home in your imagination. Use a mirror, or a taperecorder. Meet people in your imagination over and over again. When you are introduced, repeat the name over again so that you will remember it. Say it over to yourself. Meet the person's eyes. Practise a firm handshake. Know what you look and sound like. You are as good as anyone else and better than most.

Conversation

Conversation is just talking to people, isn't it? Surely anyone can do that? Well not necessarily. There is an *art* to conversation. To some people that means thinking of clever things to say. For you the art may just be in being able to talk to someone without appearing nervous or stuttering. It's all practice. For some people it comes naturally. They know how often they should meet someone's eyes, and when to stay quiet.

You might have to practise these things. You might have to learn to relax while you are talking, so that the person talking actually sounds like you instead of someone else. Conversation isn't easy, and there is much more to it than just thinking of something to say. There's all the body language as well. How do you sit? Do you lean forward or sit upright? Do you smile? Do you stare into someone's eyes or do you look and then look away?

All these things will come naturally if you can just relax and *be yourself*. Forget about the details. Practise sitting comfortably and being relaxed. Everything else will come naturally.

* * *

All of these social events are easy if you are relaxed and calm. Remember our introductory chapter. Practise relaxation at home. You can then use it on these social occasions. If you are relaxed, or can become relaxed after the initial excitement, then there are no problems. Don't avoid social events. You should enjoy them and it is worth the effort and all the practice.

5
Entertainment

Entertainment is about enjoying yourself. Of course you should be able to go out and have fun just like anyone else. It is an important part of life. But it can be difficult for some of us. Entertainment means being in wide open spaces with lots of other people and sometimes, more and more these days, lots of noise. You can feel trapped if you are in an auditorium and a long way from the exit, or if the atmosphere is formal. If you have problems with public places, and if you have been avoiding them, it is time you took your courage in both hands and found out why.

People who are nervous do not enjoy hanging round the house. They would like to be out and about enjoying themselves, but they are inhibited by the uncomfortable physical feelings that they get in public places.

Let us look at some aspects of public entertainment:

- Cinema
- Theatre
- Concerts
- Sporting events
- Swimming pools
- Clubs, societies and evening classes

Cinema

Let's start with the cinema because in a way it's the least demanding of the different forms of public entertainment. Demanding, that is, of the members of the audience. All you have to do is sit there and you can come out at any time you want to. What could be easier?

The cinema is an excellent place to start your career as a

participant in public entertainment, but it isn't quite as easy as it sounds. You are in an auditorium and there may be a lot of other people there. The soundtrack is very loud. It is dark and the images can be disturbing. And sometimes sitting in the dark watching the screen can make you feel slightly dizzy.

The worst thing of all is that you actually have to go out. You have to travel to the cinema. You have to mix with crowds of people. You are in public and on view out in the great outdoors. You may feel exposed and alone, that this is an alien environment even though you are in company. There is the opportunity for things to go wrong. No wonder you feel apprehensive.

We know all about going out. We know all about anticipation. We know how to do relaxation exercises and to prepare for going out. There is only one way to cure those feelings you get when you do go out, and that is by actually *doing* it. Make up your mind to go out. Choose a film that you really want to see so that it will be worth your while. Go with someone who understands that you may feel a little apprehensive. Take your time, and go at a time when the cinema will be least crowded, perhaps early in the evening.

When you get there, buy your ticket and in you go. There will be plenty of empty seats so that you can choose one near the exit and sit at the end of the row. It's easy. You may feel a little disorientated at first, particularly if it has been a long time since you were at the cinema. Just sit quietly, relax, breathe slowly and enjoy the experience.

If you feel panicky, don't worry. Nothing can happen to you and no one can see you. Panic away. Those feelings will settle down if you give them a chance. Use the cinema to practise managing those feelings. Decide that you aren't going to leave the cinema before the end unless you absolutely have to. Sometimes you might feel that you will make a public exhibition of yourself by shouting out or doing something unexpected. These are irrational feelings, even though they are very disturbing. Many nervous people have them. Don't worry, you won't do anything to draw attention to yourself. That is guaranteed.

Don't just go to the cinema once. If you are going to use the cinema to practise going out and enjoying yourself, you have to go often. You have to make a habit of going and practising your relaxation and managing those odd feelings. You have to build on your experience. Go at a busy time. Sit in the middle of a row. Make things more difficult for yourself. Go with friends. Make an evening of it. You may find that you begin to enjoy it.

Theatre

What is the difference between the theatre and the cinema? It is the same sort of building—the same auditorium. The same sort of things happen and it is the same kind of audience. Only a nervous person will be aware of the difference. And there is a big difference.

The answer is that the theatre is more formal, and that is a big difference for a nervous person. You can't easily leave in the middle of a scene without making a commotion. You don't normally eat sweets. The formality makes the event seem more prestigious and so more intimidating. That makes the adrenaline flow, so unpleasant symptoms are more likely to occur. And that starts spiralling up: you anticipate symptoms so you get symptoms.

A visit to the theatre can be very enjoyable. You should go if you have the opportunity. If you go and are prepared, you will enjoy it. Events such as plays can change the way you look at life. You have to look at ways of minimizing the trauma.

First of all, you can book your tickets and thus choose your seats in advance. Choose seats that suit you. Choose a quiet night in the middle of the week. Decide who you are going to go with and make sure they are sympathetic. Choose a comedy or a farce. Very dramatic plays can have long moments of great *drama*, where the tension is palpable in the audience as well as on the stage. Be prepared in your mind for difficulties and know that they will be shortlived and that you will be able to manage them. And build on your experience. Go to a more serious play next time, and keep going.

Concerts

There are all sorts of concerts, from the most raucous of pop concerts to serious classical music concerts. Some are informal, and some are very formal. There are no general rules, but there are some things all concerts have in common. Pop concerts or informal concerts are relatively easy. The problem, if there is one, is with the crowds. The concert will be in some sort of auditorium or arena, and you might feel trapped. Stay close to an exit.

A formal concert is more formal than the theatre. There is a certain amount of ritual involved in classical music concerts, and *you mustn't cough*. You may feel uncomfortable during the slow movements. You might feel that you are choking. This is where your relaxation training helps greatly. If you forget about the music for a few minutes and concentrate on your breathing you will be able to relax away unpleasant feelings. But practise at home. Imagine that slow movement. Think how you might feel. Relax. And if the performance is good enough you might just be transported away from the mundane problems of your own body and actually enjoy yourself.

Sporting events

Participation

You will feel more relaxed and comfortable if you are fit. Fitness brings with it a sensation of wellbeing. You might like to consider taking up a sport, or going back to a sport that you had given up. That sport could be anything from carpet bowls to horseriding or to a team game like football. And I would include 'keep fit' classes as a sport.

The problem is in getting into the sport, because if you are nervous you will naturally be apprehensive. You will have to go to a strange location and meet new people. Then your performance may be judged. You might make a fool of yourself. Most of all you might be trapped in a situation you can't control. All very difficult.

But it's worth the effort. Find a sport that you really want to do. You can't manufacture interest, so find an interested friend. Breaking into new groups on your own isn't easy, so go with someone else. Find out where the sport is taking place and have a look at it first, so that you know what to expect.

Then you just have to go along. Physical activity is very distracting so you will soon forget about your own physical symptoms. Sport is something you usually do every week, and repeated experience 'burns out' the unpleasant sensations. Make a start and stick at it. Sport it informal and enjoyable, and for the nervous person very confidence-building.

Spectating

There can be few more pleasant things to do on a sunny Saturday afternoon in summer than to go and support your local cricket team. Even in the winter when the wind is howling, you can support your local football or rugby team, or perhaps your hockey team.

You can go when you want, and come away when you want. You don't have to speak to anyone. And you can shout and applaud a bit if you want to let yourself go. Of course you are away from home and in an open space so you may feel a little exposed and maybe a little shaky on occasion, particularly if it is a big event and you are in a grandstand. And it's surprising how the excitement can affect you, even when watching important sporting events on television. It doesn't matter so long as you know why it is happening so that it doesn't frighten you.

Swimming pools

Swimming pools deserve a separate mention because they are different; they are very accessible and a good place to go for recreation. Swimming can be good fun too, but there are special hazards for the nervous. The main one is being separated from one's clothes. There is that white 'lavatory tile' atmosphere to contend with as well, and what about the attendants? Some of them can act as if they own the place. The whole thing can be a little intimidating.

Every pool has its own routine and its own system for changing and keeping clothes. Once you find out what it is, and you get to know the attendants, you can feel very much at home in your local pool. It's that first visit, or couple of visits perhaps, that are so daunting. You just have to go. Decide that you won't stay long, and use the experience to learn about the pool and its organization. Find out when it is quiet. Sometimes a pool has almost no one in it, and at other times it is full of school parties.

Go at the quiet time. The swimming is not the problem, it's the changing, the shower before you enter the pool, and the grand entrance into the water that can be daunting. Just decide that you *are* going to do it, and when. Tell the attendants that it is your first time there. They will be much more helpful than you expect. Have a quick dip and come home. You will feel much better for it.

Remember, people are always involved with themselves and their own affairs. They don't spend their valuable time watching you. Don't feel conspicuous or overconscious of your body. Just look after yourself and don't even think about what other people may think about you.

Have you thought about having swimming lessons? Learning to become confident in the water will help your overall confidence. Most pools have learners' or improvers' classes, and they would be pleased to see you. Learning or improving at any sport is a good idea. It is all about confidence-building—just what you need.

Clubs, societies and evening classes

Clubs

If you have a special interest of any sort, joining a club or society or going to an evening class can be a good idea. Some people enjoy them, some do not. You can feel very at home in a club, or you can find it rather claustrophobic. Certainly, any club or society will welcome you with open arms. They are always only too delighted to get new members. Clubs meet in all sorts of different places and that can be a problem, because the venue can sometimes be offputting, particularly if it is a school classroom. The same applies to evening classes.

Again it is the anticipation which is the worst part of going to a club. You can feel ill all day before going out. You can have butterflies, and the diarrhoea feeling. It gets worse before you leave to go. But why? The experience is a bit like going to a social gathering. It is intimate, but a bit artificial. You won't like everyone there, and then the members will all have friendships and relationships and you will be a bit of an outsider no matter how welcome you are made to feel.

It takes time to get over these difficulties. Consider the first visit to be just an investigation. Try to go with someone, even if you don't know him or her in advance. Just try to get through the evening as comfortably as possible. Relax and breathe slowly. Don't be tempted to talk too much. After all you are just an observer. If you like what you see and hear, you can go back and take a bigger part in the proceedings. Be prepared for a rough time at first. You might become a member for life, so it is worth the effort it takes at the beginning.

Evening classes

Evening classes are much the same as clubs and societies, perhaps because they take place in schools at night. This in itself can be intimidating, perhaps because it brings back memories of childhood, or perhaps because one feels an outsider.

A course of evening classes may last about six weeks. It might be cookery, playing the guitar, painting or anything. It is somewhere to go. It might be a start for you. Choose something active, rather than a course of lectures, something you are interested in and enjoy. Just enrol and away you go. You will have the same difficulties with anticipation, but you know how to deal with them now. Consider your classes as an exercise in going out.

* * *

Entertainment isn't just one of life's extras. It is important to have some recreation, some relief from the tedium of life. You deserve a break. *Just make a start—anywhere. Have the courage to do that and you won't regret it.*

6
Animals

Animal phobias are quite common. Many people feel panicky when confronted by a dog or cat, or it might be an insect or spider which causes the problem. Sometimes this phobia can be so strong that it interferes with everyday life. That is the time when something has to be done about it.

There are many things which can be done about these phobias and we shall now see how one can go about overcoming them. It is important that you do overcome your phobia because it may be your phobia alone which is keeping you from leading a normal life. It may be that your fear of a particular animal is at the back of your mind all the time, and this is completely dominating your life. That would be a great shame, because you can come to terms with your phobia, overcome it, and begin to lead a full and complete life.

Let's take each animal or insect in turn:

- Dogs
- Cats
- Cows
- Spiders and insects
- Snakes
- Birds
- Mice and rodents
- Fish

Dogs

The dog is probably the most common animal we meet in the course of our everyday lives. There are always plenty of them about, and they very often seem to run freely without anyone being in charge of them. When you go to someone's house, as likely as not there will be a dog there, so if you have a dog phobia there can be real problems. We can use a dog phobia to illustrate some of the points common to all similar phobias.

What is a phobia? Why should you be afraid of dogs? It is a very complicated subject, and there are many books written about it. In brief the answer is that you *aren't* afraid of dogs in general. You may be afraid of *some* dogs, particularly if they are large and fierce and likely to bite you. Fortunately there aren't many of these around so you don't have to worry about them. But that isn't the problem. The problem is that you would be just as afraid of a Pekinese; you would have the same fear reaction. You aren't actually scared of it at all, but you get the same physical reaction as if you were terrified. How do you deal with this reaction?

If you are walking along the street and a dog appears the way dogs do, just keep walking and ignore it. You will have those terrible panicky feelings with your hand shaking and your stomach churning, but so what? The dog can do you no harm and will not even notice you if you ignore it. Keep your hands out of the way and if it comes up and sniffs at you, keep walking. You will feel uncomfortable, but nothing else, and when you have finished your encounter you will feel very proud of yourself.

If you are in someone's house and they have a dog, it will take an interest in you because you are in its house. If you are unlucky it will jump up on you and that will be difficult for you. Don't panic. Breathe slowly. Keep your hands in your pockets or at least out of the way, and speak slowly and quietly to the dog. It is traditional to say that it is a good dog, even if it is a monster and you hate it. Tell the owner that you aren't comfortable with dogs, and he will remove it. If he doesn't, quietly insist. Wait for your panic feelings to subside as you know they will do.

If you have to go up the driveway of a house and there is a barking dog, or worse still, if you have to go to the door of a house with a barking dog before actually going in, perhaps as part of your occupation, you can feel very threatened. It can be a nightmare. It will take courage because the dog can make a terrifying racket. Of course you must prepare for this situation by learning to relax and practising in your imagination. Even so, it isn't easy, but you must take your courage in both hands. Avoiding a difficult situation will not help. Practise walking up drives where there is no dog and imagining that there is one. What does it feel like? Nearly as bad as in the real situation? Perhaps the real situation isn't all that bad.

Just walk confidently up the drive. The dog will bark but so what? Ring the doorbell. The dog will go berserk but you are prepared for that and for the feelings of panic which follow. You ride out the panic as the door is opened. The owner will probably control the dog, but you will still feel bad. Concentrate on slow breathing and relaxation, and pretend to be confident and comfortable. Look into the distance. Keep your hands away from the dog.

You are now managing your dog phobia instead of it managing you, but you have to build on your success. Go and visit a friend with a dog often so that you can practise all the time. Choose someone with a small dog—an Alsatian might be a bit much to begin with. Anyway, have you ever wondered about those people who march around with Alsatians shouting 'Heel Brutus! Back, boy!' I think you might be better off with your dog phobia!

Cats

Cats are nice soft small creatures with big claws and sharp teeth. A cat phobia is just the same as a dog phobia so you have to manage it in the same way. Cats outside aren't such a big problem because they are fastidious and leave you alone. It is different in someone's house. Here the cat will usually try to sit on your knee, just for badness. The prospect of a close encounter with a cat will produce in you all the unpleasant symptoms we now have come to associate with a phobia.

Expose yourself to a cat as often as you can and always practise relaxing, talking slowly, breathing slowly and being yourself even if you don't feel much like yourself. If you act naturally, other people will treat you normally as if nothing were wrong.

Cows

You don't meet cows all that often, but if you enjoy walks in the country a cow phobia can be a bit of a problem. Many people have this and it is perhaps the most understandable phobia of all. Cows are large creatures and they are very curious, particularly if they are young heifers. Heifers are skittish and playful and if they see you coming they will charge up to you and push to get a good sniff at you. That can be somewhat disconcerting for someone who isn't used to it.

You may go for walks scanning the horizon for cows, fearful that you may meet some. You may also be concerned that in amongst the cows there may be a bull, and that isn't impossible. Bulls are genuinely dangerous and you would be well advised to avoid them.

A field of heifers is another thing. They are friendly animals and will do you no actual harm. If they crowd round you just shout at them and they will draw back. If you run at them, they will run away. If you stand still they will come right up to you and sniff at your feet. That can be rather touching, and if you can, it is worth just standing still and making friends with the cows.

Don't run away from cows. They will run after you. Walk slowly and they will walk after you, breathing heavily.

Spiders and insects

Of all insects, it is usually spiders that people are phobic about. Technically a spider isn't an insect so we should make a distinction. A spider phobia is very understandable. A spider is a horrible creature, and in some countries they can be dangerous, so concern about them is rational. In this country spiders are harmless to us.

If you are in a shed, or in the bathroom, you may come upon a spider unexpectedly and that can trigger off all those unpleasant panicky feelings. The sensations can be overwhelming. All you want to do is to run away. But try to stay calm and where you are if only for a few seconds. You have to re-educate your nervous system, so start by counting to ten. Breathe and relax for ten seconds.

You can't arrange to meet a spider every day so you will have to make do with a picture. Get a child's spider picture and put it on your wall. Get used to living with it. Get something more realistic and look at that while you do you relaxing. Just get used to spiders. You will soon control your fear reaction, and in time overcome it, but it will take work. The same is true of other insect phobias.

Snakes

You never see a snake in the wild in this country, so your phobia is confined to zoos and aquaria, and to snakes appearing on television. You can avoid contact with snakes, but you may come upon them in some circumstances unexpectedly and that can give you a bad moment or two. All that has been said about spiders applies to snakes. Just keep your composure and leave quietly and you will be fine. Snakes are slow movers so they won't jump out unexpectedly and alarm you.

Some people are fascinated by snakes and keep them as pets. It takes all sorts.

Birds

Birds—budgies and the like—flap their wings and look predatory. It is this wing movement that alarms people. Alfred Hitchcock realized how intimidating these creatures can be when he made the film *The Birds*. By and large birds will avoid you if they can, but they can't in confined places, and flying free in someone's house they can be very frightening. You don't encounter that situation very often, but if you do just ask the owner to put the bird back in its cage.

Let's include hens as birds, which is after all what they are. You can meet farmyard hens in any country area and you just might have a hen phobia. Here it isn't the fluttering of the wings that produces the panicky sensations, it's the hen itself just doing its own thing. A hen phobia can mean that you avoid country areas and for some people that can be a major liability. You have to work on your phobia. Learn to relax and to breathe. Then work to 'desensitize' yourself with gradual exposure first to pictures of hens, and then hens themselves. If your hen phobia is disrupting your life, you must know that it can be cured and you must work at it. You can get back to a normal phobia-free existence if you want to.

Mice and rodents

In this modern age we don't see too many of these creatures. No one likes rats, but a lot of people do quite like mice and even keep them as pets; some people even keep rats as pets. Then there are gerbils and hamsters and guinea-pigs which many children keep as pets. All of these can produce a phobic reaction.

A mouse phobia must be one of the best-known there is. Everyone knows of the woman standing on a chair to get away from a little harmless mouse. But, as anyone with a phobia knows, it isn't a joke. You know exactly what she feels like. And by now you must know what she should be doing about it.

She should be relaxing and controlling her breathing, and if necessary walking away slowly.

If you meet a hamster or a gerbil, don't immediately rush away. Stand back from the cage by all means, but try to stay where you are and wait for your panicky sensations to settle down. And field mice in the country are beautiful little creatures with big ears. They move slowly and aren't in the least bit afraid of you. You could learn to love them.

Fish

Fish can't be too great a problem because they live in tanks and can't get close to you. None the less there are a lot of them about and they will be present in many of the homes you visit. I know of one girl who felt that fish were a threat and who put a cloth over a fish tank in a house where she stayed. That is one way of dealing with the problem, but there are others as you will realize by now. Try to come to terms with your phobia so that you can forget about it and go back to leading an entirely normal life.

* * *

Now we are making progress. We can see that there is a way forward and we should be feeling more confident. We can deal with our many problems, *if we go about it the right way*, and if we work at them. And work we must, because the rewards are tremendous.

7
Ceremonies

It is very difficult to avoid ceremonies. We all go to weddings and funerals and other events. There is no reason why we should avoid such events because they can be very enjoyable. It may be the only time when families get together and they are important occasions. Then there are graduations, prize-givings and civic events. All have to be attended, but they can be traumatic for the nervous person.

With a little practice and attention to detail ceremonies can become manageable and then even enjoyable. Of course you have to make a little effort and have the courage to attend what can sometimes seem to be, for you, a traumatic event.

Let's look at some aspects of going to ceremonies:

- Weddings
- Funcrals
- School events
- Public ceremonies
- Speeches
- Church
- Court appearances and jury duty

Weddings

Your own wedding

You will probably get married one day. If you are already married you can skip this bit because you will already have gone through this important ceremony and survived it. Yes, weddings are survivable, one way or another. I know of bridegrooms who swear that they only survived their weddings by the use of copious quantities of alcohol.

You shouldn't have to go to these lengths to survive your wedding. In fact, most people feel that they have thoroughly enjoyed the ceremony and cannot understand what all the fuss was about. It is great to be wise after the event, but I know of no one who wasn't apprehensive before their wedding, and why not? It is a solemn and important occasion.

Ceremonies are made solemn to underline their importance. That means a lot of dressing up and ritual. You may feel that this event is of great importance and go to the lengths of wearing morning dress or a white dress if you are the bride, but you will at least wear your best suit or smartest dress even if you think it is a personal affair and of no consequence to anyone else.

Weddings have a momentum of their own. What begins as a small affair for the immediate families rapidly expands because so many people want to wish you well and be involved. The nervous person finds himself or herself at the centre of a rapidly expanding ceremony. You might view your coming nuptials with growing alarm.

You don't have to worry; weddings have been happening for years and you don't hear of people collapsing, forgetting their lines or making a fool of themselves. The event is planned to go like clockwork, and a lot of professionals work very hard to see that it does. Your role will be almost passive. You just turn up and go through a programme that you will have rehearsed in advance.

Of course there are speeches and the like. There is a certain amount of formality, but everyone there is wishing you well and the goodwill is almost palpable. Even the most cynical of bridegrooms or brides will be carried along on the tide of happiness that is inevitably found at weddings.

Also, everyone knows that the participants are apprehensive. The mother of the bride is expected to shed a few tears. Everyone expects to be embarrassed by the telegrams, and there are always a few minor hiccoughs in the organization. People make allowances, they expect to enjoy the event and are not in any sense critical.

All you have to do is to look after your own part. Learn to relax. Practise and rehearse your bit until you are fed up to the back teeth with it. You must know that you can do it automatically. We will deal with speechmaking later in this chapter, but if you really don't want to make a speech, then don't. It is your day and you can do what you want within limits. If you are the bridegroom you can just stand up and say 'thank you' to everyone who has wished you well. You don't have to be a stand-up comedian.

If you are a nervous person and you are a bride or a bridegroom, expect to be apprehensive to begin with on your wedding day. Everyone is, but you will settle down when things get underway and enjoy yourself.

Other people's weddings

Sometimes you will be the guest at someone else's wedding. You might even have to participate as the best man, bridesmaid or the mother or father of the bride. The problem here, as in all of the other formal situations which we are discussing, and in classical music concerts, is the terrible task of having to sit in the audience when there are formal events or speeches going on. It is worse if you know that soon you are going to have to participate by making a speech or becoming involved in the ceremonies.

It's that dreadful feeling of choking and panic you feel as you sit trapped in the audience. You feel dizzy, your heart is pounding and you can't breathe or swallow. It's absolutely terrible. It can turn one of these happy events into a nightmare.

If you have had experience of this sort of thing you will know that it's no joke. You can feel that you're actually going to die, or that at least you will make a fool of yourself and have to rush out. You might even shout out and spoil the ceremony. Of course these things don't actually happen, but the fear of them is none the less real.

What can you do about them? Well first of all decide that you are actually going to go and weather the storms. Prepare. Practise and rehearse as always, and just take things easy. Don't get flustered. Walk slowly, talk slowly and practise looking calm no matter how you feel. It is when you are in the thick of it that you need your preparation most.

The anticipation and the first few minutes are the worst. Take your time and concentrate on getting through the start of the service. As time goes on things will get better. Remember to rehearse everything in your mind, even the small talk to distant relatives.

Funerals

The tradition surrounding funerals is different in different parts of the country. Sometimes women attend the graveside, and sometimes they don't. Nowadays cremations are common, with the ceremony taking place in the crematorium. Like weddings, funerals are emotional events though in this case the emotion is one of sadness.

If you are attending a funeral, you will have known or perhaps loved the person whose funeral it is. So will the other people present. There is a common grief. That fellow-feeling will help you through the day. If you are grieving for someone you have loved, don't be afraid to let your emotions show. People will respect your personal grief. The ceremony is there to help you. It has its own momentum, and again there are professionals to do the organizing. You have to go through certain rituals, some of them as old as time. It gives you a sense of the continuity of life, and that can be a comfort.

People often wonder how they are going to manage a funeral. The task seems daunting. Often it is the person most affected, usually the widow or widower, who manages best and here is a lesson for us all. If the job has to be done it will be done, and done well.

School events

Events in school involving one's children can be very difficult. The parent is under the scrutiny of the children, or at least feels himself or herself to be. You wouldn't want to let the side down by making a public exhibition of yourself, would you? It adds an extra stress to an already stressful situation. And then the event takes place in school, an alien environment. Schools are unpleasant places for those who aren't used to them. They have a peculiar atmosphere of their own.

So you might have to go to the school concert or the school play, or perhaps a prizegiving. You feel anxious for both yourself *and* your child. And then the place will be full of other parents chattering away, many of them known to you and not all of them the sort of people you might choose to socialize with. It's all a bit much.

So you know what the difficulties are going to be: what can you do about them? You can't avoid the event because your children are expecting you to be there. If you have to go, you have to make the best of it. Do what you always do. Arrive early so that you can get a seat that suits you. You don't always have to get an aisle seat or one near the door. As you become more confident over time you can start to be a bit more adventurous. Be prepared for that false camaraderie and the peculiar atmosphere, and for those dreadful speeches or the terrible music.

Remember that many parents get very emotional when their own children, or even other children are performing in school concerts or plays. It is a very touching experience. You might find this type of strong emotion difficult to manage, but it can be done.

Use the time before the event starts to practise your relaxation and your breathing. The first five minutes are the worst so decide that all you have to do is to get through them. When you have done that get through the next five minutes in the knowledge that for every five minutes you get through it is five minutes less that you have to get through, and nearer to the end. If you divide up the evening in that way you will get through it with the minimum of difficulty.

Public ceremonies

These events can prey on the mind for months. Apprehension can grow and become very distressing, but as always the event isn't as bad as you think it will be. These affairs are made to be as formal as possible with all the main participants dressing up and with processions and ritual. The event may boost the morale of the establishment running it, but it's hell for anyone who is nervous. It's the formality that gets to you.

If you are very lucky you might never have to participate in a civic event, particularly if you don't seek public office, but you might have to attend as part of your job or your hobby. You are unlikely to be the centre of attention. These formal occasions aren't all that formal, are they? If things really become very bad you could simply walk off. Of course things won't go wrong, but the knowledge that you have some control over what happens will help you to stay put no matter how bad you may feel. And if you aren't the centre of attention you can ignore the proceedings and concentrate on your breathing and relaxing.

Speeches

Your own

You can get through most of your life without having to make a speech, but there comes a time when you will be asked to make one and to refuse would be embarrassing. You just have to get on and do it.

You are never more alone than you are when you stand up to make a speech, even if it is only to be a few words in front of half a dozen people. You can be sure that your mind will go a blank and that you will feel panicky. Everyone feels like that. Public speaking is accepted as being very difficult.

Books have been written about the art of public speaking because it is a big subject. Learning how to do it isn't easy and few people do it well. The feelings you and everyone else get when you stand up to speak are similar to those you get before any difficult event, except that they may be a little worse.

The secret of successful speech-making is in the preparation. You have to allow for the fact that your mind will go blank and that you will have to go on 'autopilot' for a few moments. That means that you have to do what any actor would do, learn your lines and rehearse. You have to practise in front of the mirror, record your speech and listen to it. If you try to do it cold, it will be a disaster.

You need notes. But don't try to read your speech. That just sounds like a speech being read. Paradoxically, if it is to sound impromptu it has to be prepared and practised and you have to have notes to which you can refer if you 'dry up'. Good clear notes on paper, or better still on cards, will give you the confidence to carry on. Don't be afraid to take your audience into your confidence if you dry up and say something like, 'Wait a minute, I've lost my place.' You'll probably get a laugh.

It's like everything else, you have to *know* that you can carry on if the worst happens. You have to know that you can continue to speak even if you have a panic attack. You have to prepare for that dreadful moment when you stand up and every face turns towards you. But you *can* do it.

Don't be too ambitious. A joke that goes wrong is a disaster. If you don't get a laugh what do you do? Tell anecdotes that are relevant and will interest and entertain if you like, and then say what has to be said.

Other people's speeches

It can almost be as difficult for the nervous person to have to listen to someone else making a speech as it would be for him or her to make one. There is an element of tension in any speech and that rubs off on the audience. There is a period of quiet and attention when a cough would be noticeable, so that you get that feeling that you are about to drown. If can be very unpleasant until there is a response from the audience, a laugh or applause, or anything. The ice is broken and you can settle down. It is those difficult first few minutes which you have to get through, and that's when you need your relaxation and breathing exercises.

Church

Church can be a difficult place for the nervous person. It has all the formal atmosphere of any ceremony. It's worse if you aren't used to going to church and it all seems a little strange. It's hard to prepare for a church service, but you can weather the storm. All right, you may not feel that you can walk out in the middle of a hymn or prayer, and some non-conformist prayers seem to go on forever, but you are never really trapped. If the atmosphere is unfamiliar, sit in the balcony or near a door and you may be more comfortable.

Court appearances and jury duty

No one likes appearing in court. Again it is a formal event with all the trappings of a ceremony, all contrived to make it seem important and to make the outsider ill at ease. More people seek medical certificates to be excused jury duty than for any other reason.

You may have to appear in court as a witness, or a member of the jury, or perhaps as the accused. (I would try to avoid the last!) When most people go to court they are going into the unknown. That is the way it should be. You can go to the public gallery of a court at any time; in fact it might be worth doing that initially if you are particularly nervous. But most people don't have the time; if you haven't, just turn up on the day.

Try to find out from friends or from your solicitor what goes on in the particular court you are to attend. What do you call the judge? What are the procedures? Expect that when you arrive, no matter what your role is, you will have to wait. Waiting seems to be part of the legal system.

If you are on a jury you will have a job to do and you will have to get on with it. If you have panic attacks or the like, just ride them out. When you become interested in the case, you will begin to concentrate and everything will settle down. Listening to the summing-up is like listening to a speech. But you will find that court is less formal than you expect.

If you are a witness, the best policy is strict honesty. You have to come across to the jury as a reliable honest person, and if you exaggerate or express opinions the lawyer on the other side will make a meal of you. He can do nothing if you are honest and straightforward. If you are nervous, the judge will help you.

* * *

Ceremonies are constructed to somehow give support and dignity to events and the people involved in them. They are formal and can be intimidating for the nervous person, but they are part of life. We have to attend some of them. They can be enjoyable. Even court attendances can be interesting and enjoyable. Just do the best you can. Ceremonies are there to bring people together, so those assembled have a lot in common, and will give mutual support. Don't be embarrassed to let your emotions show.

8
Shopping

Some people would list their main hobby as shopping. Others find it a daunting business fraught with difficulties. They feel panicky and unwell in some shops and may not be able to go into shops alone. They live with the constant fear of a panic attack.

You have to go shopping. It is an essential part of life and now we live in the consumer society it is more important than ever. All the techniques that have been described can help you, but one thing is certain, at the end of the day you will have to take the plunge and go out into that shopping precinct.

Let's look at some aspects of shopping:

- Corner shop
- Supermarkets
- Queues and the checkout
- Banks and post offices
- Video cameras and detection equipment in shops
- Shoplifting
- Shop assistants: wrong change and bad service

Corner shop

Let's start with the easiest form of shopping. It may be that you have simply got out of the habit of shopping. You may have found that you get unpleasant panicky sensations when you go shopping, and so you have just started to avoid doing it. Or perhaps you don't completely avoid shopping, you simply find it unpleasant and do as little of it as you can.

How are you going to overcome this problem? How are you going to become comfortable in shops again? It isn't easy. It involves practice, and the least threatening and most pleasant sort of shopping for most people is the old-fashioned corner shop. There must be one in your area. It might be a grocer or a newsagent. It doesn't matter which.

What you must do is to start the habit of shopping again. Start going to the shop every day, at a quiet time at first. Don't get into too much conversation. Just talk about the weather like everyone else. Expect that you will feel shaky when you are walking to the shop. Expect a tremor in your hands. It doesn't matter. You are going to go in and you are going to buy something.

Keep going to the shop every day, but go at a busier time and buy more. Shop for someone else. Stay and talk about football or politics. Be prepared to ride out panic attacks and unpleasant sensations until you are absolutely used to them and they are an everyday event. It is the *fear* of your symptoms that causes you the trouble, more than the symptoms themselves and once you have made friends with them you will start to become comfortable in shops again.

Supermarkets

Most shopping these days is done in large supermarkets or in city stores. That can be either a nightmare or a boon to nervous people. It can be a boon because it means that you only have to shop once a week and that can be done at night in the company of your husband or wife. You don't have to talk to anyone and you can get the whole thing over as quickly as possible.

The disadvantages are that the vast impersonal store and the crowds of people can be threatening. Then there are queues at the checkouts that we consider later. The idea of shopping in one of these places can be terrifying.

Don't worry. Start with your corner shop until your confidence comes back and then go to the supermarket at the least busy time. Do your shopping and leave. Have a shopping list if that will speed things up and avoid any indecision. Go with someone else to give you moral support. If you panic, ride it out. No one will notice and you will survive. Nervous people are born survivors.

Queues and checkouts

In supermarkets and in big city shops there are always queues at the checkouts. That can be a nightmare for the nervous person. In a queue you feel trapped. You have to wait your turn and shuffle dutifully towards the checkout. Once in the checkout channel you really are trapped, and the assistant may be less than helpful.

You have to use your skills of relaxation and breathing if you are to survive this ordeal, but it is survivable. No one is watching you. No one is interested in you. They are all too busy looking for their money and checking their trolleys. You can genuinely relax. Be deliberate, take your time and don't get flustered. Don't let any assistant hassle you.

City shops can be worse. On a Saturday they may be jammed with people and you are constantly being jostled. The tills are permanently busy and there are queues everywhere. At times like Christmas you may find it necessary to go to the big shops, and anyway it's good to do some shopping in city shops from time to time.

Of course you have to manage travelling. It might be best to go with a friend or with your husband or wife. You have to manage the streets as well as the shops, and the streets are busy with people and cars. If ever you are likely to have a panic attack it is in the city.

Always remember that you can come to no harm. No matter how bad you may feel, nothing can actually happen to you if you 'keep your nerve'. If you feel panicky, stand quietly until it passes, no matter where you may be. If you are in the checkout queue, it is just the same. Stand quietly and wait for it to pass, *and it always will*.

One other tip: if you feel bad, think why. Are you hungry?

Is your stomach upset? Are you cold? If there is a physical reason for the way you feel, it is much easier to manage and you will find it easier to relax. Organize your trip to the city. Decide where you are going to go, what shops you want to visit, and how long you are going to stay. Take some sweets in case you get hungry. If you are going to stay in the city over a mealtime decide where you are going to eat, but remember that eating in public can be traumatic for some nervous people.

As always, the first time is the worst. Once you get into the habit of shopping in the city it will cease to be a problem.

Banks and post offices

These establishments are rather formal and they tend to have queues, so they can be difficult. They are often smaller than shops and seem to be more enclosing. Some people don't like going into them, particularly if they are busy. Again it's a matter of practice, of going in when they are quiet and then starting to go in when they are busier.

The post office is worse than the bank. It seems to have succeeded in constructing the most intimidating system possible for serving the public, with long queues for the few windows open and multiple rails to enclose those queueing. It isn't very pleasant for anyone, and certainly not for a nervous person.

[On the general subject of the way things are put together, architects may at last be designing things with the disabled in mind, but they don't give much thought for people with phobias. Who wants to go up in a glass-sided lift, or walk across precarious unsupported pedestrian bridges? Some people certainly don't, and you may be one of them. You might occasionally have to take the long way round.]

Video cameras and detection equipment in shops

If you haven't been shopping recently you may be surprised by some of the detection equipment now in use in big stores. Garments have great buttons riveted on to them and there are video cameras everywhere. A nervous person might feel that he or she was under constant surveillance and that wouldn't be far from the truth.

In this day and age that is something we will probably have to live with. It is certainly something we can get used to, but it isn't easy. There is always that fear in the back of the mind that we might accidentally trigger off a detection device and sound all sorts of alarms. In practice that doesn't happen because the devices are very sophisticated and are supposed to be foolproof.

Shoplifting

Shoplifting is not the problem—unless you're a shoplifter, that is—it's the fear of being *wrongly* accused of shoplifting. Modern shopping with its self-service and open shelves can be very intimidating. Most of us have accidentally taken something, or almost taken something, from a shop without paying. It does happen, but it is a rare event.

You feel uneasy and concerned about these things because the temptation is so obviously there. Goods are displayed and are meant to be picked up. Even so, you feel guilty and this is made worse by those cameras. Remember that you can't be arrested for shoplifting until you have left the shop, so it is possible to pause before you go out and mentally check that you have paid for your purchases.

What about that fear of being wrongly accused of shoplifting? You might be completely innocent and yet be the centre of a great public scene. Unlikely! Store detectives and shop managers are highly trained and don't easily make that sort of mistake. They don't want any adverse publicity.

If some event does happen that you find embarrassing, try not to get flustered or to do anything in a hurry. Certainly don't let yourself be 'frogmarched' through the store. If there is a misunderstanding try to clear it up on the spot. You can give your name and address and show your shopping bag to the store detective if necessary. Take your time and think about what you are doing. Only do what seems reasonable to you after you have given it your careful consideration.

Shop assistants: wrong change and bad service

Being a shop assistant is a hard job with long hours and inadequate pay. It should not be too surprising if at the end of a day he or she becomes irritable, and we should make allowances. That is different from accepting bad service.

Some shop assistants have a habit of ignoring customers, or serving them while talking to their friends, or being rude. Sometimes that is due to bad training, but there is no reason why we as customers should put up with it. Some shop assistants learn how to intimidate nervous customers, so that these customers may not want to complain about short change or bad service.

The problem is that if you are intimidated and don't do anything about it, it will annoy you for days or months. You will never shop in that store again and that is bad both for you and the store. You really must have the courage of your convictions and complain at the time. Do it politely but firmly, and if you don't get satisfaction ask to see the manager and complain again.

If you get home and still feel bad about something, write to the manager and make a detailed complaint giving whatever evidence you may have.

* * *

Shopping should be enjoyable and you should be able to do it in comfort. If shopping bothers you, do it as often as you can. Practice makes perfect. You can start going to only a few shops, but as time goes on arrange to go to more and more shops at busier times. Go with a friend, but as confidence returns go alone. Plan ahead. Decide what shops you want to go to and where you are going to eat. Decide how you are going to travel. Make sure you have money and a cheque book. Ignore surveillance equipment such as video cameras, but check that you are not open to a charge of shoplifting, though this is extremely unlikely. And enjoy your shopping.

9
Holidays

Holidays are important. They are not some sort of optional event we can take or leave. We have to get away from our routine life, particularly if that life is made difficult by anxiety and tension. One can holiday at home, and many people do. The advice in this book might help them. Other people like the excitement, better weather and total change one gets on a holiday abroad, and there is no reason why a nervous person shouldn't take advantage of the great bargain that a continental holiday offers.

Holidays are not as relaxing for everyone as one might hope. First impressions of a resort often don't come up to expectations when one arrives tired and irritable. It takes a while to unwind, but if you go expecting to have a good time, you will, and you will have an experience to remember the rest of your life. And think of the confidence it will give you. You won't be able to wait for next year.

Let's look at some aspects of taking a holiday:

- Deciding where to go
- Planning and preparation
- Airports and airplanes
- Boarding, taking off and landing
- Tour company representatives
- Excursions and shopping
- Emergencies

Deciding where to go

If you are going to go on a holiday the first thing to do is to decide where you are going to go. That is an important decision for anyone, but particularly for the nervous person because he or she needs to get it right first time with the minimum of fuss. Holidays in this country are reasonably straightforward, but going abroad is another matter.

Travel agents aren't all that helpful. They can usually give you all the brochures from the big travel companies and they can do the bookings, but they don't give a great deal of advice. You have to make your own decisions on the basis of those brochures. It can be very difficult, particularly if you are going on an air/hotel type of holiday in the Mediterranean. There is so much choice.

It is what the brochure doesn't say which is important. If the hotel has a pool, the brochure will say so. Interpreting the brochures is like understanding the handouts from an estate agent. 'Ideal for the young at heart' means noisy and crowded. 'Rapidly expanding' means they're still building it. You have to read and weigh every word, and that includes the flight information. The wise avoid night flights.

The most important decision that you make is that you are going to go. Make that decision, pay your deposit, and you are committed. No going back now, and that's a good thing. You have to go through with it and you will.

Planning and preparation

Planning seems to be very important for nervous people. You have to get everything right in advance so that you can be sure that it goes smoothly. That means getting the passports and making the bookings in good time. It includes aspects like international driving licences and traveller's cheques. Buy holiday clothes early and allow time to do some research into your holiday. Find out where it is you are going and what you can expect to find there.

You should be able to anticipate problems and think of ways of dealing with them in advance. When you go on holiday, things should not be completely strange to you. You should have some idea as to 'what comes next', so that there are as few surprises as possible. That means asking questions of travel agents, talking to people who have been to your resort before, going to the airport for a visit with someone who has travelled often and who can show you where everything is.

Knowledge creates confidence. It is uncertainty that makes one feel panicky.

Airports and aircraft

Airports used to be places frequented by rich people flying off to exotic destinations. Now they are more like cattle-markets with all sorts of people just going on their holidays. There is nothing exclusive about them and most people have experience of using them. If you have avoided flying because you are nervous, you have missed one of the joys of this generation and its time you did it. Flying seems like a terrifying prospect, but really there is nothing to it. You must believe that. Take it as a matter of faith.

How can going up in the sky be a simple matter? How can a nervous person do it at all? It's easy. Unlike almost anything else, once you have started you can't get off. The thought of that might make you nervous, but even if you are nervous, you will definitely arrive at your destination. Your only problem is getting yourself on the plane.

Airports are busy places, particularly in the summer. You will have done some homework and visited the airport of your departure. You will have studied the departure procedure. You will know where you check in. You will have magazines with you for the departure hall and the flight. You might have pills for diarrhoea if that is a worry, and you might even have taken medication to settle you down during the departure. You will certainly have practised relaxation and breathing exercises, and you will have rehearsed the airport procedure in your imagination.

Charter aircraft travel fully loaded. They have to if they are to be economic, so you can expect a full aircraft. The seats are close together and there is little leg room. Not particularly pleasant, but it is worth the nightmare just to get to the sun. Expect the worst and you will be pleasantly surprised.

Boarding, taking off and landing

The airport procedure is simple. You arrive, find your check-in desk and queue. Then you check in your luggage and get your boarding card. You will need your passport for this. You then sit in the airport lounge until your flight is called. If there is a delay it will be announced and flight information is shown on television screens.

Now you have to queue for passport control. You may be feeling a little nervous and shaky, but you have anticipated this and you are actively relaxing. Then you go through the hand-luggage check and passport control to another wait in the international departure lounge, feeling a little like James Bond only slightly more nervous. It's a great rollercoaster ride. You might visit the duty-free shop, or you might be more comfortable sitting quietly just breathing in and out.

Your flight will be called, and even though you have a seat number, there is a rush. You are off, walking briskly down the walkway. You are on the conveyor belt. There is no going back now, and why should you? This is an adventure. You hand in your boarding pass and board the aircraft. The seat numbers are over the seats, but someone always gets it wrong and there is confusion. People tend to be flustered. You haven't time to be worried.

When everyone is settled there is a delay, and this might be the worst part. The engines start up and the plane lumbers towards the runway. Just work consciously through the relaxation exercises and practise slowing your breathing. Don't hold the arm-rest until your knuckles go white. Relax and breathe. Enjoy the show when the stewardesses demonstrate the safety equipment.

Now comes take-off. The plane waits at the end of the

runway and tests the flaps, so that you may see part of the wing move up and down. Then the engines rev, the brakes are released and the plane accelerates, as does the heart-rate of every passenger including yours. It lasts a matter of seconds, and then you are in the air and climbing. Take-off is over. It will be exactly the same on the way back, only then it will be better because you will have already done it once and it will be familiar.

Landing is the other tricky bit. You might start to become a little apprehensive as you near the time for landing. Nothing has happened to you during the flight. You haven't made a fool of yourself. You haven't tried to get out, and anyway you couldn't because the doors of a pressurized aircraft won't open in flight. Now the engine note changes and you begin to descend.

The 'seat-belt' and 'no smoking' signs come on and you can see the ground getting closer. There is a noise as the undercarriage comes down. The aircraft seems to go very slowly and it almost seems as if it might fall from the sky. It won't. It will just get lower and lower, but you know that it will be over soon. All you have to do is to sit quietly, breathe in and out and wait for the bump as the wheels hit the runway. That is a great moment, and many a planeload of passengers has broken into spontaneous applause.

Tour company representatives

Travel companies have a vested interest in ensuring that you enjoy your holiday, and for that reason they employ representatives at the different resorts. It must be a difficult job on occasions, because holiday-makers are determined to enjoy themselves from the second they arrive and won't tolerate any hitches or problems. Everyone, and that includes you, is a little uptight.

There are good reps and not so good reps, but all are willing to help you with problems, so if you have any particular difficulty you should see them. The point is that even if you are abroad you aren't abandoned. There is someone to help you who knows the lie of the land. It will, however, take no more than about one day for you to feel really at home so you shouldn't anticipate problems.

Excursions and shopping

You can't spend all of your time in the hotel. Well you can actually, but there are other things to do even if your hotel does have everything on the spot. Your tour company will have excursions and there will be shops nearby for buying souvenirs. You want to get out and about a bit, and forsake the beach for a while.

If you go on an excursion booked by your tour company, the coach will pick you up from the hotel. You will have the problems of bus travel with its lack of toilets and the like, and you will be doing the equivalent of travelling away from home when you leave the hotel, but you can do it. If you have been adventurous enough to go on the holiday, you can be that little bit more adventurous and go on a tour. All the same rules apply and what you really fear just doesn't happen.

Shopping isn't a problem either. Every shopkeeper will speak enough English to be able to sell you something. Forget about haggling and the other things you hear about. Just decide what you want to buy and go and pay for it. Leave your shopping to the end of your holiday when you will have mastered the currency and the local peculiarities. After two weeks you will feel as if you have known the resort all your life.

Emergencies

Emergencies rarely happen. If something should go wrong you will be able to deal with it, and there is always that tour company rep. to help you. Take sensible precautions. Take a first aid kit with you as well as simple medicines from your chemist to cover more common ailments. Take the travel brochure so that you can check what you get against what you have booked. Have a copy of your holiday insurance with you and make sure it allows for air evacuation of sick or injured members of your party. Know how to reach your rep. and find out the addresses of local doctors and chemists. Above all have spare money available in some form so that you can pay doctor's or hospital bills if necessary. As always, a little planning and thought will cover most problems, so that if anything untoward does happen, you at least know where to start sorting it out.

* * *

Your annual holiday is one of the most important events of the year. It is your treat for struggling with your nerves for the rest of the year. It isn't easy, and certainly not any easier than being at home, but the compensations are great. It is two weeks away from your routine grind, and we all deserve that. Just have the courage to go. Take a deep breath and book the holiday of your choice. You won't regret it.

10

Getting on with Other People

One of the most important things in life for all of us is our ability to get on with others. It is important in our work, our marriage, our relationships with the people we meet in our everyday lives. For most of us getting on well with others is instinctive and easy, but for some it is a skill which has to be learned and practised.

There have always been shy people, and shy people can appear awkward or even aggressive. It is the art of meeting other people's eyes just the right amount, of saying just the right things at the right time, of being sure that the effect which we have on others is the effect we mean to have that shy people have to learn.

Let's take each of the following in turn.

- Family
- Others
- Doctors
- Girlfriends or boyfriends
- People at work

Family

Let's start with the family because that is where we all start, literally. Our first relationships are with our parents and our brothers and sisters, and these relationships can be the most uninhibited and thus the most stormy we ever have.

We shall include our relationship with our wife or husband in this section, because that is a different relationship as well, quite unlike any other as the law recognizes. These relationships are made in heaven and we have little choice but to make them work, and for the most part we do that very well.

These close relationships are not static. They change all the time. Initially we are totally dependent on our parents, but as time goes by we become less dependent and more critical, and in some case our parents end up being dependent on us. We may begin by hating our brothers and sisters, but in the end blood is thicker than water and we may become more accepting and less competitive. Marriage can be a stormy affair, but it changes too and usually for the better. Most marriages last a lifetime even in this turbulent age.

These close relationships depend upon honesty and understanding, on genuine give and take. A truly selfish person cannot have an honest relationship because he or she will contribute nothing and take everything. If you want to make a relationship work you have to work at it and always try to see the other person's point of view, and see how you appear to them. A relationship is a balancing act, and you cannot be too self-effacing because that offends, and you cannot be too dominating because that is destructive. It is worth working to create close family relationships, because in times of trouble it is upon the family that we depend.

Others

Our relationships with people outside the family are a different thing altogether. We keep some of ourselves in reserve, keep some of our guard in place. We cannot be totally honest in this situation because that would embarrass others. We have a public face.

The important thing is to make sure that that face is the one we really want to show, and that it is not distorted by our shyness or nervousness. If meeting other people feels awkward we may have to practise our skills of communication. This is a big subject and is dealt with very fully in other books.*

*Such as *How to Improve Your Confidence* and *Overcoming Tension* (Kenneth Hambly, Sheldon Press).

Doctors

We all consult doctors from time to time, but nervous people may do so more than some others because of problems caused by their nervousness as well as for the usual complaints. Doctors, and I include psychologists who are not medically trained but who have special training in nervous problems, can be a great help to those troubled by their nerves.

I know that there are some general practitioners who are not helpful, but they are in the minority, and even if you have had unfortunate experiences with doctors in the past, you may find a new awareness of the problems, both physical and psychological, that can be caused by nerves.

Furthermore, there is now more in the way of help available. Some general practices have attached psychologists, or community psychiatric nurses (CPNs) who can help people with nervous problems. Never be too embarrassed or too shy to go to a doctor and ask for help. You might be surprised at what can be achieved.

Girlfriends and boyfriends

Perhaps this is a subject for the young, for people starting out on life's peculiar journey. As we go through life we learn, and even if we are in a situation later in life where we have to establish new relationships, we should have more confidence and we should be able to handle them more easily.

For a younger shy or nervous person, relationships with members of the opposite sex can be very difficult. That is because we have to put so much of ourselves 'on the line'. We have to risk so much which is intensely personal, and we have to live with the possibility of rejection. None of this is easy for a sensitive person of either sex.

There are no easy answers. We have to work out our own relationships, but it is worth remembering that most boys and girls have the same insecurities, and they want the same things. They want to be happy, to lead a meaningful and fulfilled life, to get married and stay married and to have children. Much of what happens in adolescence and after is preparation for that.

Remember, too, that some people are better at some things than others. The guy who can 'pull the birds' at fifteen may make a rotten husband, and the girl who is desired by all at eighteen may not be everyone's idea of the ideal wife. Your time will come.

In the meantime work at putting your true personality over, using the techniques described in this book, and practise being a relaxed person, someone with whom most people are comfortable.

People at work

For many of us much of our time is spent at work. Work can be difficult for nervous people, but much of that difficulty may be due to our relationships with others, with our fellow workers, or with bosses or with those under us. These relationships are hard both to establish and to maintain.

Any group of people establishes relationships naturally. Some will be dominant, some lead by example, some prefer to be led. You can be an expert in one area, and completely incompetent in another. Relationships in the workplace are a juggling act.

Relationships change. If you go on holiday, things will have changed when you come back. You have to go through a procedure known as 're-entry', where you re-establish those relationships that have changed in your absence. Relationships at work, like any others, require a little give and take.

You must decide where your threshold of tolerance is, and defend that position. That is the 'bottom line' for you, the position from which you will not budge. All other positions are negotiable, and you will trade off the advantages for you against the disadvantages until you have established a tenable position. If you can do that with firmness, so that others know where you stand, life is much easier.

* * *

Life is really all about relationships with other people, and these require constant work and attention particularly if we are nervous. Relationships, either intimate or business, have to be made to work, and that takes care and effort. The payoff is happiness and contentment, so it is worth that effort.

Appendix: About you . . .

Life isn't easy if you are a nervous person. The problems that you have may lead you to live a restricted life. There may be things that you feel that you cannot do, and there are many things that you can do but that cause you to have severe and unpleasant sensations. At times you may be in despair. Does it really have to be like this? Does being nervous mean that you will have to take a back seat in life and, most important of all, does it mean that you are any less of a person than someone who isn't nervous?

Certainly not! Life is there to be enjoyed, and there is no reason why you can't lead as full and as happy a life as anyone else. And as for being less of a person than someone who isn't so nervous, the reverse is true. People who are nervous are the way they are because they are sensitive and aware, and they have great courage. People who aren't nervous will never appreciate just how much courage nervous people show as they go about their everyday lives. Even the most simple tasks can require great effort and courage.

You have that courage. You have ambitions as yet unfulfilled. You want to lead a normal life. Is that possible? The answer has to be yes, we know that it is possible because so many other people have overcome their problems and returned to a normal contented life. The thing that is stopping you is only *yourself*.

That is not a criticism. You have been trying everything you know to overcome your problems, but you may not have been trying in the right way, and you have been trying by yourself. There is nothing more destructive than a feeling of isolation and loneliness. Yet you are not alone. Nervousness, or rather the problem of an overactive nervous system, is one of the most common complaints that I see in my own general practice. You would be greatly surprised to know just how common it is, and by some of the people who are afflicted by it.

Why do so many people suffer in silence? If it is so common, why isn't it a topic of conversation every day? Why don't people talk about their problems? Why is there a conspiracy of silence? The old taboos still linger, and psychological problems remain in the closet. That is a tragedy if it means that people like you suffer in silence, perhaps even feeling alone and somehow unworthy, while arrogant and brash people take over the world, our world, and trample over the feelings of those who should inherit the earth.

It is time you did something about it. You can't change the big world, but you can change *your* world. You can make it better. All that is wrong with you is that your nervous system has begun to overreact to the situations you are meeting. Over a period of time this has eroded your confidence and you are now getting problems. What are you going to do about it?

You have made a start by getting this book. You have to do the exercises at the beginning, but then it is a matter of attitude. Know that you are as good as anyone else. Know that you have courage and determination. Know that you have quality, and that many don't. Know that you have talent, and that it would be a sin to waste it. You have to use your courage and determination the way others in your position have done in the past. You have to go out and do the things that you *think* you can't do.

It is only by doing this that you can overcome your difficulties. Once you have done something, it will be easier for you to do it again, and your symptoms will be less distressing. Each time you do something that is difficult for you, you are a winner. From now on you can only win. Things will get better and better, easier and easier. You will have turned the spiral round. Now it is downhill all the way.

It is a slow process and there is a long way to go, but you can do it just as others have before you. Believe in, trust, and have faith in yourself and your ability. Now make a start, anywhere you like. Your journey through the rest of your life starts now. Good luck!

Index